The EARTH Book

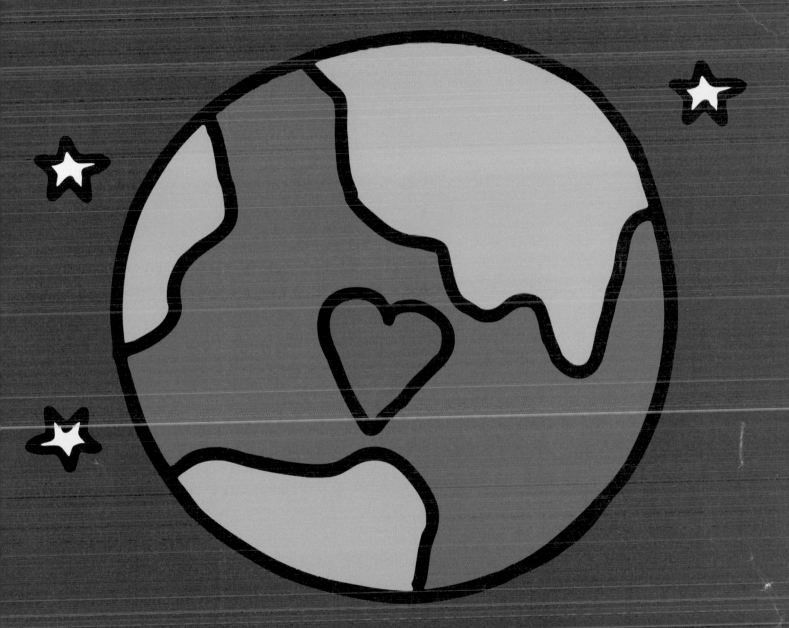

The EARTH Book

TODD PARR

SCHOLASTIC INC.

To my mom and dad, for putting me on Earth.
To Liz and Gerry for going to Las Vegas and to
Megan for asking me if I had ever thought about
writing children's books.

Special thanks to Liza and Fatimah.

Love, Todd

I take care of the earth because I know I can do little things every day to make a BIG difference.

I use both sides of the paper

and bring my own bags
to the market because...

I love the trees

and I want the owls to have
a place to live.

I turn off the faucet
while I brush my teeth

and use less water
for my baths because...

I love the fish

and I want the oceans to stay blue.

I take the school bus

and ride my bike because…

I love the stars and I want the air

to be clear so I can see them sparkle.

I try to eat every bite on my plate

and save my leftovers because...

I love watching things grow

and I want there to be
enough food for everyone.

I remember to turn off the lights

and shut the refrigerator or
to save energy because...

I love the polar bears

and I want the snowmen to stay cool.

I throw garbage in the trash can

and recycle glass, aluminum, paper, and plastic because...

I love to walk barefoot in the grass

and I don't want to move to Mars!

Most of all, I help take care

I want us ALL to be happy and healthy!

Every one of us can help protect the earth and make it feel good.

Remember: if we take care of it, it will take care of us. Love, Todd

ISBN 978-0-545-85623-2

12 11 10 9 8 7 6 5 4 3 2   15 16 17 18 19 20/0

Printed in the U.S.A.   40

First Scholastic printing, March 2015

Todd Parr is the author of more than thirty books for children, including the *New York Times* bestselling *The I LOVE YOU Book*. He lives in Berkeley, California.

Also by Todd Parr:

The I LOVE YOU Book

It's Okay to Be Different

The Peace Book

We Belong Together

The Mommy Book

The Daddy Book

The Grandma Book

The Grandpa Book

The Family Book

Reading Makes You Feel Good

The Feelings Book

The Feel Good Book

For a complete list of all of
Todd's books and more information, please visit
www.toddparr.com and www.planetcolorbytoddparr.com.